HALLOWE'EN FUN

ABIGAIL WILLIS

ILLUSTRATED BY ANNABEL SPENCELEY

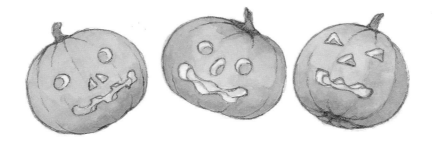

Kingfisher

KINGFISHER
An imprint of Larousse plc
Elsley House, 24–30 Great Titchfield Street,
London, W1P 7AD

This edition published by Kingfisher 1994
10 9 8 7 6 5 4 3 2
Copyright © Grisewood & Dempsey Ltd 1993
This edition copyright © Larousse plc 1994

A CIP catalogue record for this book
is available from the British Library

ISBN 1 85697 275 5

Phototypeset by
Southern Positives and Negatives (SPAN),
Lingfield, Surrey
Printed and bound in Spain

Designed by: The Pinpoint Design Company

CONTENTS

101 SPELLS FOR SPECIAL OCCASIONS

SCARABIAN FRIGHTS by I.M. SCAREDSTIFF

GRIMM'S HAIRY TAILS

Welcome to **Hallowe'en Fun!** Open up this book of spooky delights and feast your eyes on some great things to make and do. Keep a pencil, scissors, glue and a ruler handy – everything else you need is listed with each activity. So, choose a costume, throw a party, and have a terrific Hallowe'en!

CREEPY COSTUMES

A good costume is essential at Hallowe'en, and here are some great ideas for how to make your own. You could be a witch, complete with hat and broom, or maybe you'd like to be a spider – see over the page for the spookiest spider outfit you've ever seen, plus ideas for mummy, skeleton and ghost costumes.

WITCH

You will need

Black fabric, needle and thread, green tinsel, stick-on stars or yellow fabric, false nails, card, black paint, a black bin liner, a wooden pole, twigs, Velcro®, glue, nail polish, string

2 Decorate the cloak with stick-on stars or glue on cut-out fabric shapes. Sew or glue the tinsel along the front edges of the cloak.

3 Now decorate yourself! Glue on false nails, or paint your own nails a gruesome colour.

Make your own magic broom by simply tying a bunch of twigs to a pole with string.

1 Cut out the black fabric to make a large cloak. Attach a 5-cm strip of Velcro® tape on both sides of the cloak's neck so you can fasten it.

To make the witch's hat:

1 Cut a brim from the card so the inside circle fits just over your head.

2 Roll another piece of card into a cone shape. The base should fit over the inner circle of the brim.

3 Make small cuts in the brim and stick the tabs to the inside of the cone.

4 Cut a wide strip from a black bin liner and cut slits along one side.

5 Tape this 'hair' into the cone of the hat and trim a fringe in front.

SPIDER

1 Take three pairs of black tights (the thicker the better) and cut them into six 'legs'.

2 Stuff the legs with plenty of scrunched-up newspaper and attach the top of each leg with a safety pin to a strip of strong black fabric long enough to be tied around your waist. Remember you only need to make six legs, as your own two make it eight in total.

3 Wear black leggings and a black sweater or leotard, and decorate your top with a web design using thin masking tape.

4 Glue two pipe-cleaners to a headband and attach two painted card eyes.

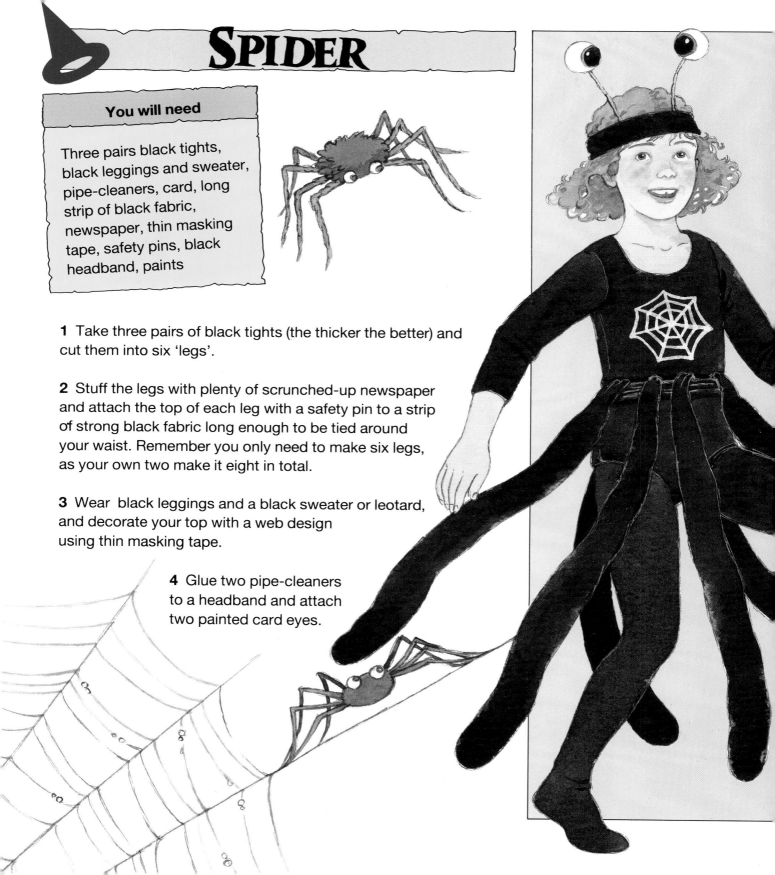

▼ How about being a bony skeleton? You'll need to dress in black and then, using white tape or fabric paint, stick or paint on 'bones' – just follow this picture. For a really effective look, paint your face like a skull – see page 17.

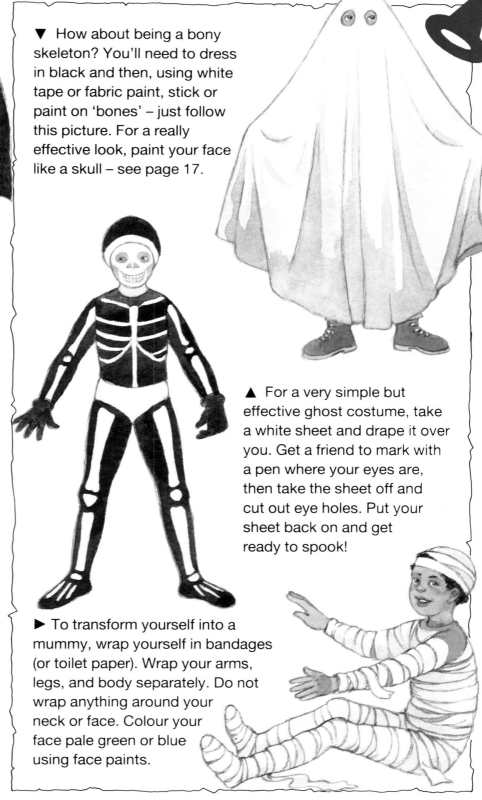

▲ To make a slippery bat outfit, cut a black bin liner along its seams and open it out. Cut along one edge to make bat-shaped wings, and attach to your arms with wool threaded through the plastic and tied at the elbow and wrist.

▲ For a very simple but effective ghost costume, take a white sheet and drape it over you. Get a friend to mark with a pen where your eyes are, then take the sheet off and cut out eye holes. Put your sheet back on and get ready to spook!

► To transform yourself into a mummy, wrap yourself in bandages (or toilet paper). Wrap your arms, legs, and body separately. Do not wrap anything around your neck or face. Colour your face pale green or blue using face paints.

A MIDNIGHT MOBILE

When the midnight hour strikes, see the shapes of Hallowe'en come to life. Make this simple mobile and hang it up every year – with a light October breeze, and the flickering light of a pumpkin lantern, it's the perfect Hallowe'en decoration.

You will need

Thin card, tracing paper, a needle and thread, a wire coat hanger, paints, scissors, pencil

2 Paint one side of each shape using the pictures here as a guide to colours. Paint the other side of your card shape black.

1 Trace around the witch, skull, cat, bat and pumpkin onto card and cut out the shapes.

8

4 Finally, attach the other end of the thread to the coat hanger and watch your mobile swinging in the breeze!

3 Using the needle, make a small hole at the top of each shape and pull the thread through, tying a secure knot at one end.

9

A SPELLBOOK MENU

Hallowe'en wouldn't be Hallowe'en without some scrumptious, tasty goodies to eat straight from the witch's cauldron. All these recipes are great for parties or even just for yourself! Ask an adult to help you when using a hot oven or sharp knives, and remember – a witch's hat (see page 5) should be worn at all times while you are preparing your spellbook menu!

CRACKLE CACKLE CRUNCHIES

You will need

275 g breakfast cereal
225 g chocolate
2 tbsp golden syrup
Paper cake cases

1 Pour some water into a pan until it is about 2.5 cm deep and bring it to the boil.

2 Break the chocolate into pieces and put into a heatproof bowl. Put this into the pan and stir until the chocolate has melted.
3 Stir the syrup into the melted chocolate, then add the cereal.
4 Spoon into cake cases and leave to set.

WITCH'S BREW

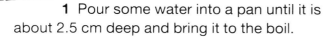

You will need

1 litre black grape juice
$\frac{1}{2}$ litre fizzy lemonade
Grapes and apples

1 Mix the grape juice and lemonade in a large glass jug.
2 Halve the grapes and take out the seeds.
3 Cut the apple into small chunks.
4 Float the fruit in the brew just before serving: by magic, the grapes and apples will look just like eyes and teeth!
5 Make a swizzle broomstick from a straw and black paper.

MONSTER SANDWICH

For a sandwich fit for a monster, use three or more slices of bread sandwiched together with your favourite fillings. Stack the slices up and carefully cut diagonally in half. Make a monster face on top of each half, using slices of boiled egg or cucumber for eyes, and a piece of ham (or anything else you can think of) cut into a fanged shape for a mouth.

BAT AND PICKLE

TOAD AND CRESS

SLIME DESSERT

You will need

Raspberry jelly
and lime jelly
Whipped cream
Smarties [R]

1 Ask an adult to help you make equal quantities of raspberry and lime jelly.
2 When set, mash each colour up separately.
3 Place alternate layers of slimy jelly into a large glass bowl.
4 Top with 'eyeballs' of whipped cream blobs with Smarties [R] in the centre.

TOFFEE APPLES

You will need

14 short wooden sticks
14 apples
450 g brown sugar
75 g butter or margarine
2 tsp white vinegar
175 ml water
2 tbsp golden syrup

1 Push a stick firmly into each apple.
2 Heat all the other ingredients in a pan until the sugar and butter have melted.
3 Bring to the boil for 5 minutes without stirring until a teaspoon of mixture hardens when dropped into cold water. Then stand the pan in cold water.
4 Dip each apple into the mixture, then stand it on a lightly buttered plate to set.

11

SCARY SKELETON

1 First trace all the shapes on the opposite page with a pencil and rub them down onto the card.

You will need

White card, tracing paper, five paper fasteners, needle and thread, pencil, scissors

2 Cut each piece out and carefully make the holes with the pointed end of the scissors. Cut along the skeleton's ribs.

3 Attach the legs and arms to the body using the fasteners. Link the two strips with the fifth fastener. Make sure that each part of the body can move easily.

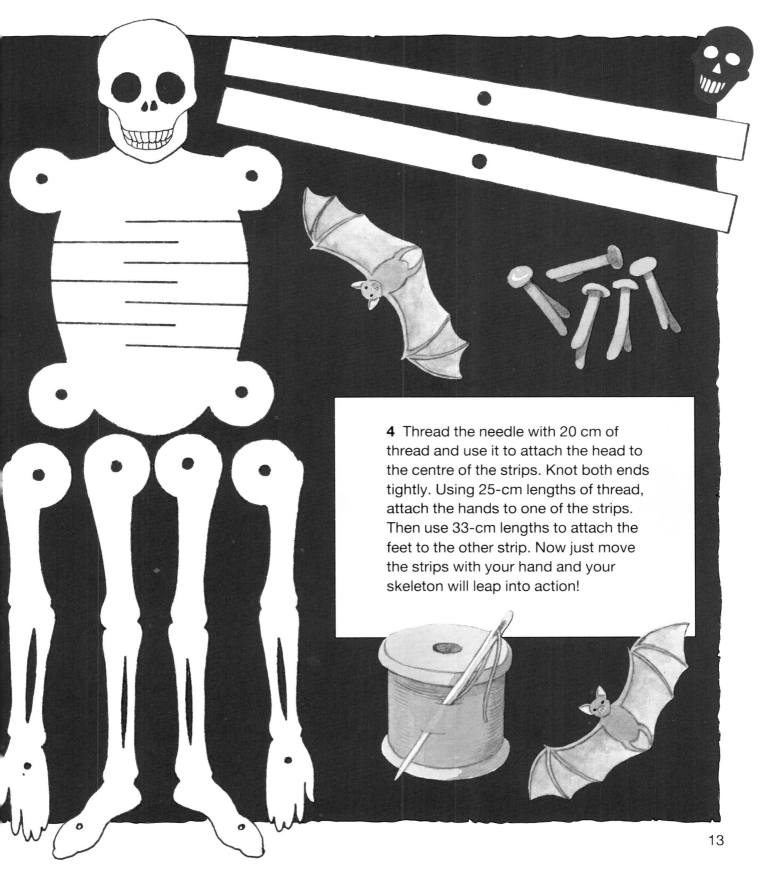

4 Thread the needle with 20 cm of thread and use it to attach the head to the centre of the strips. Knot both ends tightly. Using 25-cm lengths of thread, attach the hands to one of the strips. Then use 33-cm lengths to attach the feet to the other strip. Now just move the strips with your hand and your skeleton will leap into action!

13

GRUESOME GAMES

Hallowe'en calls for out-of-the-ordinary games to play, so here are some unusual ideas. Invite some friends to join you, and prepare to jump out of your skin!

CRAZY CREATURES

You will need

A spiral-bound notebook, felt-tip pens, a ruler, scissors

1 Draw two lines equally spaced across the first page of your notebook to divide it into three. Do this for at least eight pages, making sure that your lines are in the same place on each page.

2 Draw a different creature on each page, with the head at the top, the body in the middle and the legs at the bottom.

3 Cut along the lines so that you can turn each section on its own. Flip the pages back and forwards and make crazy creatures with mixed-up heads, bodies and legs!

VAMPIRE CHASE

This game comes straight from your worst nightmare! You'll need some red stickers and at least six people. Choose someone to be the vampire (to make them look really convincing make them the mask on page 23 to wear). Everyone else wears three red stickers. The vampire chases its victims around and, if someone is caught, the vampire takes a drop of blood (a red sticker). When someone loses all three stickers, they become the vampire and so the game continues . . .

GHOSTLY GROANS

You'll need a large space for this ghoulish game and six or more people. Pick a 'ghost hunter' and blindfold him or her. The other players or 'ghosts' circle around the ghost hunter who must try to catch one of them. When someone is caught they must wail and moan in as ghostly a way as possible and the ghost hunter must guess who it is. If the ghost hunter guesses correctly, he or she can change places with the ghost they caught. If not, the ghost goes free and the ghost hunter must try again!

FEARSOME FACES

To make a good costume look even better, try painting your face to match! Only use water-based face paints – not the ordinary paint that you use for pictures. Use bold strokes, strong colours and your imagination!

WITCH

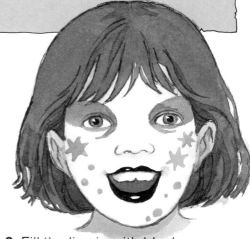

1 Put a white base colour all over the face using a damp sponge.

2 Apply purple to the eyes, sweeping the colour up and outwards.

3 Fill the lips in with black and draw on yellow stars and green warts.

SPIDER'S WEB

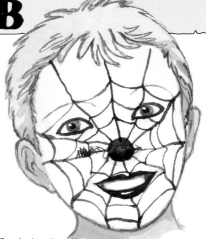

1 Apply a white base colour with a little pale green colour blended around the edges.

2 Paint the nose black and draw fine lines around the eyes and over the face.

3 Join the lines up with a spiral of black lines. Paint the lips black and add a spider.

NIGHT AND DAY

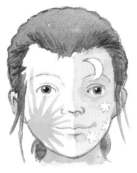

1 Paint one half of the face white and draw a sun and its rays in bright yellow.

2 On the other side, draw a moon above the eye and stars on the cheek in white.

3 Add pale blue clouds to the 'daylight' side and colour the 'night' side dark blue.

For a vampire look, paint the face white with grey shadows around the eyes. Paint the eyebrows black and make the lips blood red, adding a few red drops on the chin. Finally, paint white fangs.

To make Frankenstein's monster, use a green base on the face. Draw scars, outline the eyes in black, and paint the mouth blue.

To paint a skeleton face, use black and white face paints and copy the design below.

PARTY PUMPKINS

Without pumpkin lanterns, Hallowe'en just wouldn't be the same. The lanterns can look spooky or funny, depending on the way you cut your pumpkin. So, ask an adult to help you with the cutting and follow this easy guide!

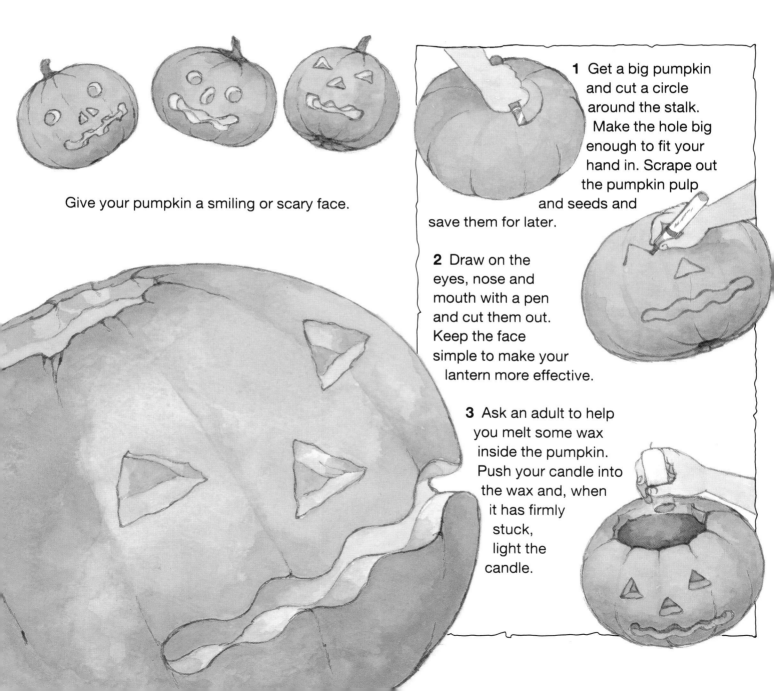

Give your pumpkin a smiling or scary face.

1 Get a big pumpkin and cut a circle around the stalk. Make the hole big enough to fit your hand in. Scrape out the pumpkin pulp and seeds and save them for later.

2 Draw on the eyes, nose and mouth with a pen and cut them out. Keep the face simple to make your lantern more effective.

3 Ask an adult to help you melt some wax inside the pumpkin. Push your candle into the wax and, when it has firmly stuck, light the candle.

A HALLOWE'EN GUY

All you need to make a spooky-looking scarecrow are some old clothes, newspaper, a pole or stick and, of course, a pumpkin. Simply stuff the clothes with scrunched-up newspaper and tie up the bottom of the legs and arms with string. Add gloves and shoes to make hands and feet and push the pole or stick into the neck of the figure. Cut a face into the pumpkin and push it onto the stick.

SEED SNACK

To use all of the pumpkin, roast the seeds for a healthy snack. Preheat the oven to 180°C/350°F/ gas mark 4.

Rinse the seeds with water. Grease a baking tray with butter or margarine and spread the dry seeds evenly on it. Bake for 10–12 minutes until golden brown. Put on an oven glove, remove the tray, and allow to cool.

19

DEVILICIOUS CAKES

A witch's kitchen is never busier than at Hallowe'en, and a really special party cake is fun to make and even better to eat! Ask an adult to help, and follow the recipe below for a delicious chocolate Witch's Cat Cake, or try making a cake in the shape of a bat or a spider's web . . .

You will need

A rectangular cake tin
  30 x 25 cm
225 g butter or margarine
200 g caster sugar
3 eggs, beaten
2 tbsp cocoa powder
  (mixed with a little hot water)
225 g self-raising flour
4 mini swiss rolls
Liquorice and other sweets

For the Icing:
150 g icing sugar
2 tbsp cocoa powder
2 tbsp hot water
50 g butter or margarine
1 tsp vanilla essence
Chocolate sprinkles

1 Preheat the oven to 180°C/350°F/gas mark 4. Beat butter and sugar together until creamy. Add beaten egg

gradually and then the cocoa. Sift the flour into the bowl and stir until the mixture is soft and light.

2 Line the tin with grease-proof paper and pour the mixture evenly into it. Bake for about 30 minutes.

3 Allow your cake to cool on a wire rack. Then cut out a basic cat shape as shown. Use the spare cake to make wedge-shaped ears.

4 To make the icing, simply sift the icing sugar and cocoa into a bowl, and gradually mix in the soft butter, water, and vanilla essence until the icing is creamy. Spread

thickly onto the cat shape. Position the ears firmly and cover with icing. Shake a layer of chocolate sprinkles over as a finishing touch.

5 To make the cat's tail, stick the swiss rolls together and to the 'body' with a little icing and cut the end of the 'tail' at an angle to form a point. Cover the tail with icing.

6 Use liquorice strips for whiskers and sweets for the eyes and nose.

For the spider's web cake, use the same recipe. Make two round cakes, sandwich them together with chocolate icing, and cover with the same icing.

Create a spider's web design by making some white icing from icing sugar and a little water. Dribble the white icing in a spiral shape then draw lines from the centre outwards using a toothpick. Decorate with a toy spider!

Cut an oblong cake into a bat shape and decorate with icing and liquorice strips.

MONSTROUS MASKS

You need the best possible mask to wear at a Hallowe'en fancy dress party. These pages show you how to make a frighteningly realistic papier-mâché werewolf mask or, if you don't have much time, make a simple Dracula card mask. Either way, you'll look sensational!

You will need

A balloon, wallpaper paste, (non-fungicide), elastic, paints, wool, newspaper, pin

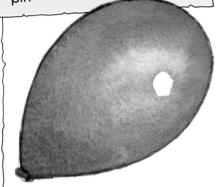

1 Blow up a balloon roughly to the size of your head.

2 Next, mix wallpaper paste with water.

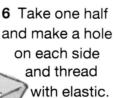

3 Tear up strips of newspaper and soak in the paste.

4 Cover the balloon with several layers of paper. Let each layer dry before you add the next.

5 When dry, burst the balloon and cut the mould in half with an adult's help.

6 Take one half and make a hole on each side and thread with elastic.

When you have made your basic mask, cut eye and mouth holes and use fresh papier-mâché to build a nose and ears. Then decorate your mask with paints and wool.

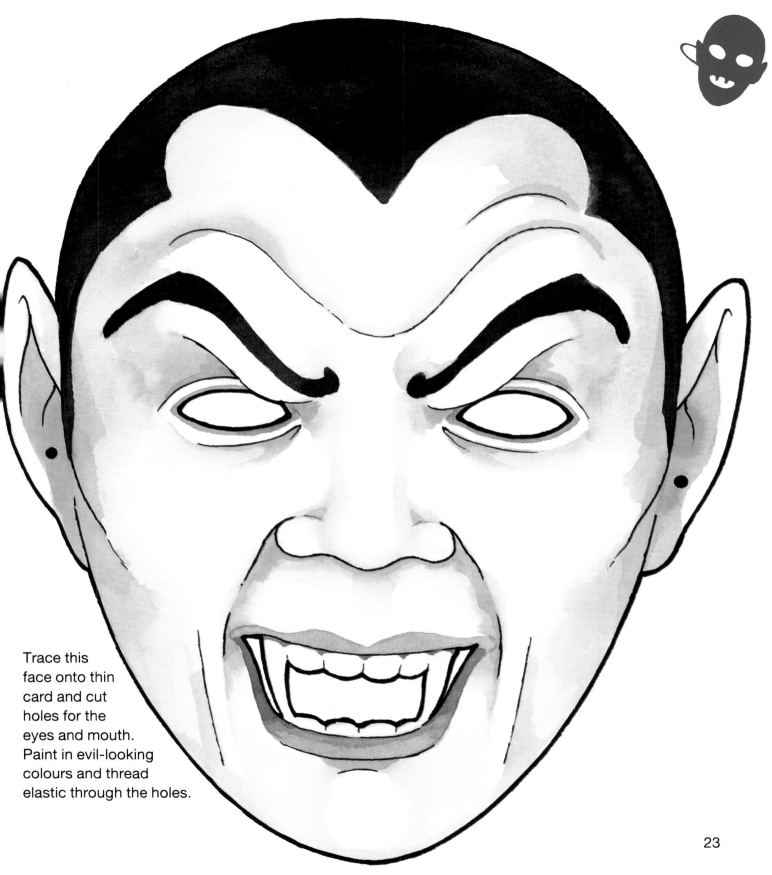

Trace this face onto thin card and cut holes for the eyes and mouth. Paint in evil-looking colours and thread elastic through the holes.

23

HORRIBLE HEADS

Here's how to make some unusual finger puppets or a mobile . . .

1 Pierce both ends of each egg with a pin, making one hole larger than the other.

2 Pushing the pin inside the egg, break the yolk, then gently shake the egg so the inside becomes runny.

3 Hold the egg over a bowl and blow into the small hole. This forces the runny egg out through the big hole.

4 Rinse your egg shell with water, then use a pair of scissors to make the bigger hole large enough for your finger to fit into.

5 Now you can decorate your ghoulish egg heads.

Paint an evil face and glue on a paper collar to make Dracula.

Paint an eggshell green. Cover with a bandage cut into thin strips for a mummy.

Create a fierce gorgon with trailing wool hair and painted face.

You will need

Five eggs, paints, a pin, fabric or handkerchief, paper, wool, bandage, scissors

For a grinning skull paint a bold black pattern on a white egg.

Use a piece of white fabric o handkerchie for a ghost head.

FURRY FIEND

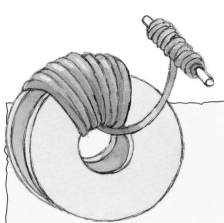

You will need

Card, thick wool, two beads, a big needle, scissors

1 Make a pompom by winding some wool around two card rings.

2 When the wool almost fills the centre hole, ask an adult to slide the blade of a pair of scissors through the wool and between the rings. Cut all the way around.

3 Tie a length of wool tightly around the middle. Remove the rings.

4 Thread lengths of wool through the body with a needle to make the legs.

5 Sew on beads to make the eyes.

TRICK OR TREAT ?

Here's how to make the witch's candy house from *Hansel and Gretel* and your own bright trick or treat bag.

CANDY HOUSE

You will need

A shoebox, strong card, colourful sweet wrappers and paints (for decorating)

Draw a plan like the one shown here onto a piece of card. It should be as wide as your shoebox lid (a) and twice as deep (b). Fold along the dotted lines to make a roof and glue the edges to the top of the box.

Cut two squares slightly larger than the width of the box. Fold and cut these to fit the side of your roof. Stick in place. Now decorate your house.

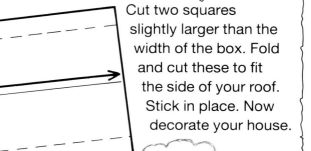

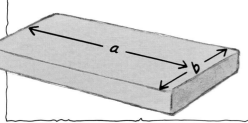

TRICK OR TREAT BAG

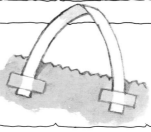

Take a large, strong paper bag. Draw and colour a bold Hallowe'en design onto it.

Cut strips of thin card and tape them firmly inside the top edges of the bag for the handles.

GHOULISH GREETINGS

Whoever gets this card is in for a shocking surprise! The card fits flat into an envelope and pops up to frighten the wits out of the (un)lucky person who opens it.

You will need

Thin card, felt-tip pens, medium-sized rubber band, ruler, scissors

1 Copy the design shown onto the card following the measurements given.

2 Colour the witch's head and cut the card out. Cut the oblong hole in the middle of the card, making sure that it is slightly wider than the witch's head.

3 Fold the card along the dotted lines, folding away from you. Push the head through the hole as you fold.

4 Loop one end of the rubber band over the notches at the back, and the other end over the notches at the bottom. This is the tricky part – ask an adult to help if you find it difficult.

5 To put the card into the envelope, squeeze it lightly together so that the rubber band stretches and the card becomes flat. It will spring back into terrifying shape the moment the envelope is opened!

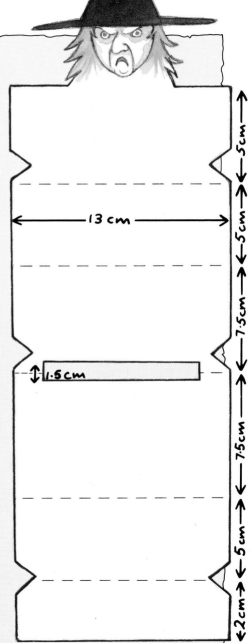

13 cm

5 cm

5 cm

7.5 cm

1.5 cm

7.5 cm

5 cm

2 cm

SPOOKY SOUNDS

Scary films wouldn't be frightening at all without spooky sounds — it's just as important to create the right noises if you want to have a really eerie Hallowe'en evening. If you have a tape recorder, try recording your own scary sound effects using the tricks shown here. Watch your friends' faces when you secretly play the tape back to them . . .

Rumbling Thunder

Take a large sheet of stiff card. Holding it by the edges, shake it back and forwards so that the middle part wobbles. This makes a rumbling thunder noise.

Hooting Owl

For a haunting owl hoot, blow gently across the top of an empty bottle.
To make higher or lower hoots, you can blow across bottles containing different levels of water.

Horses' Hooves

For the chilling sound of a ghost horse use two empty yoghurt containers or plastic flower pots. Tap them on a table to make a hollow clopping sound.

Creaks and Squeaks

Try opening a stiff door as slowly as you can for a haunted house sound effect. Or run your finger around the rim of a half-filled glass of water to make a strange, wailing noise. Shake a bag of dead leaves for a rustling effect. Often the best sounds are made with your own voice – try a cackling giggle or a deep-voiced laugh . . .

SPOOKY SHADOWS

For a flickering shadow show all you need is a bright lamp, a pale-coloured wall, and your hands.

Dog

Rabbit

Monster

Bat

Here are some shapes to try, but you will soon find yourself inventing your own. If you have recorded any sound effects, why not play your tape while you make your shadows?

Wait until it's dark, then shine the lamp on the wall and make shapes with your hands in front of the lamp's beam of light.

POEMS FOR HALLOWE'EN

Nothing is scarier than a spooky tale read aloud on Hallowe'en night. Here are some poems that will send shivers down your spine. Or why not write some yourself with mysterious invisible ink. Just dip a pen with a nib into some lemon juice and write your poem. To make the writing visible, hold the paper up against a warm radiator.

The Moon

The moon has a face like the clock in the hall;
She shines on thieves on the garden wall,
On streets and fields and harbour quays,
And birdies asleep in the forks of the trees.

The squalling cat and the squeaking mouse,
The howling dog by the door of the house,
The bat that lies in bed at noon,
All love to be out by the light of the moon.

ROBERT LOUIS STEVENSON

In the dark, dark wood, there was
a dark, dark house,
And in that dark, dark house, there was
a dark, dark room,
And in that dark, dark room, there was
a dark, dark cupboard,
And in that dark, dark cupboard, there was
a dark, dark shelf,
And on that dark, dark shelf, there was
a dark, dark, box,
And in that dark, dark box, there was
a GHOST!

ANON

A skeleton once in Khartoum
Invited a ghost to his room.
　　They spent the whole night
　　In the eeriest fight
As to who should be frightened of whom.

Song of the Witches

Double, double toil and trouble;
Fire burn and cauldron bubble.
Fillet of a fenny snake,
In the cauldron boil and bake;
Eye of newt and toe of frog,
Wool of bat and tongue of dog,
Adder's fork and blindworm's sting,
Lizard's leg and howlet's wing,
For a charm of powerful trouble,
Like a hell-broth boil and bubble.

Double, double toil and trouble;
Fire burn and cauldron bubble.
Cool it with a baboon's blood,
Then the charm is firm and good.

WILLIAM SHAKESPEARE

Witches fly skyward
Into the blackness,
Their passengers always
Cats of the darkest.
Hallowe'en is with us,
Eve of All Saints, and
Spirits are stirring.

JOHN PATON

Queen Nefertiti

Spin a coin, spin a coin,
    All fall down;
Queen Nefertiti
    Stalks through the town.

Over the sidewalks
    Her feet go clack
Her legs are as tall
    As a chimney stack

Her fingers flicker
    Like snakes in the air,
The walls split open
    At her green-eyed stare;

Her voice is thin
    As the ghosts of bees;
She will crumble your bones,
    She will make your blood freeze.

Spin a coin, spin a coin,
    All fall down;
Queen Nefertiti
    Stalks through the town.

ANON

Hallowe'en History

The story of Hallowe'en goes back over 2,000 years. For the Celts who lived in Great Britain, Ireland and northern France at that time, New Year began on November 1st. The night before, a festival was held to mark the change in season from summer to winter.

The Druids, who were the priests and teachers of the Celts, believed that witches and demons roamed the Earth on the evening of October 31st. To frighten these evil spirits away, people dressed up and lit huge bonfires.

In the AD 800s, November 1st became a Christian festival day known as All Saints' Day or All Hallows'. The night before was called Eve of All Hallows' and came to be called Hallowe'en.

Today, most people don't believe in ghosts and witches, but it's fun to dress up as one for a fancy dress party. The most important part of Hallowe'en is to have as good a time as possible!